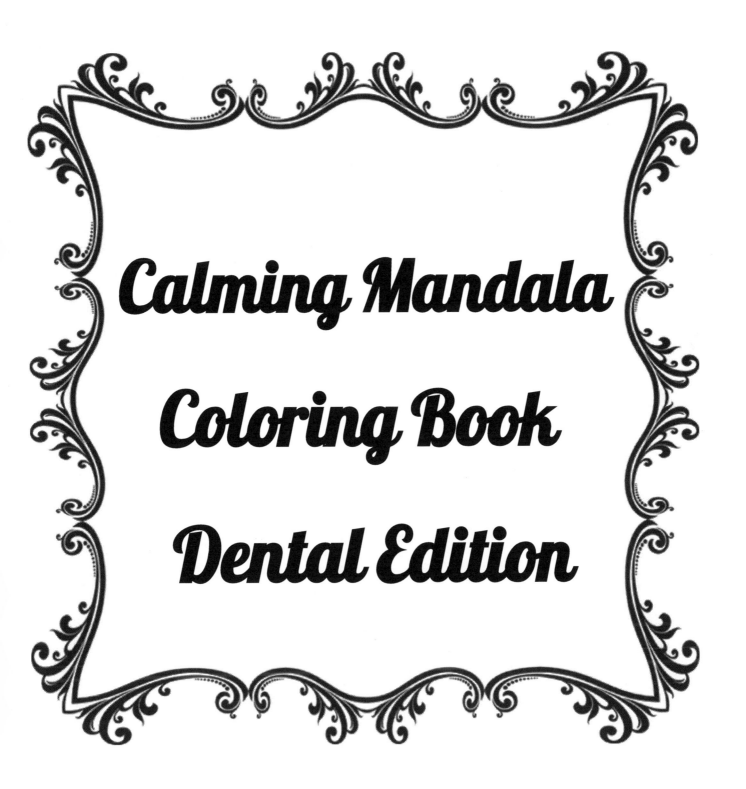

Calming Mandala

Coloring Book

Dental Edition

Illustrator - Joseph Rabie
Publisher - Evard Publishing

www.calmingmandala.com
www.evardpublishing.com

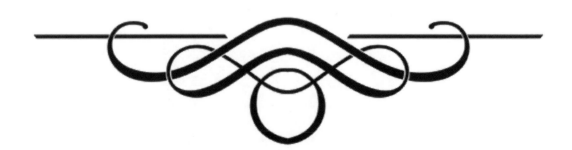

This Book Belongs to:

....

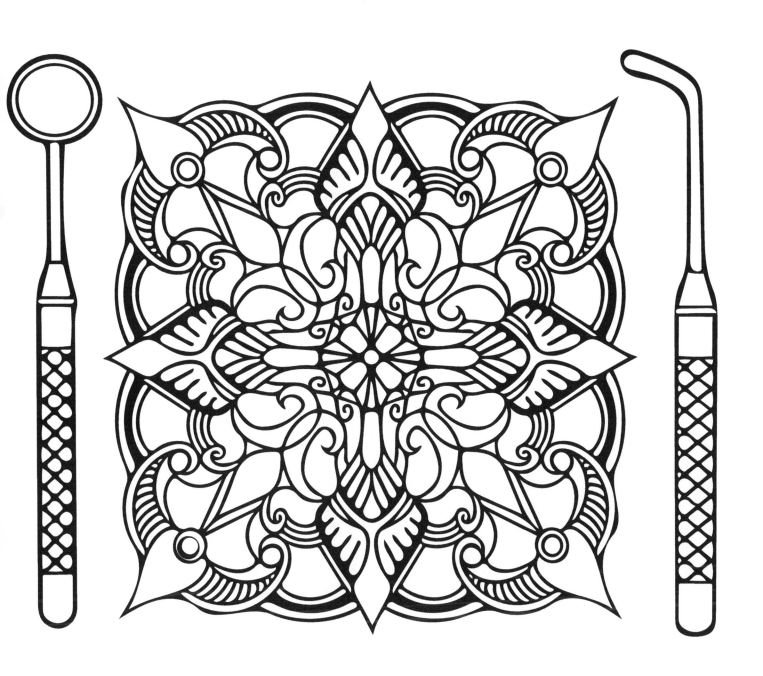

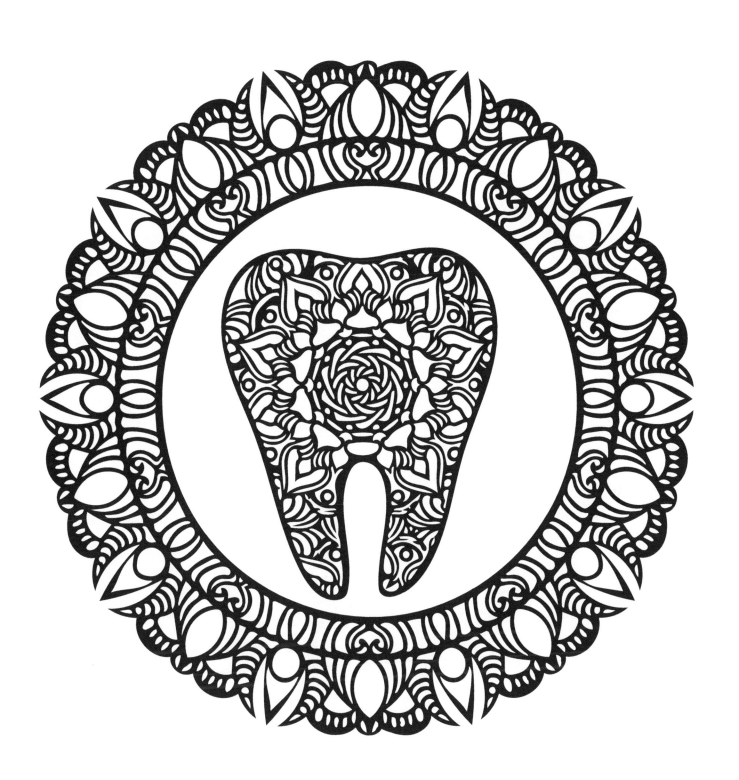

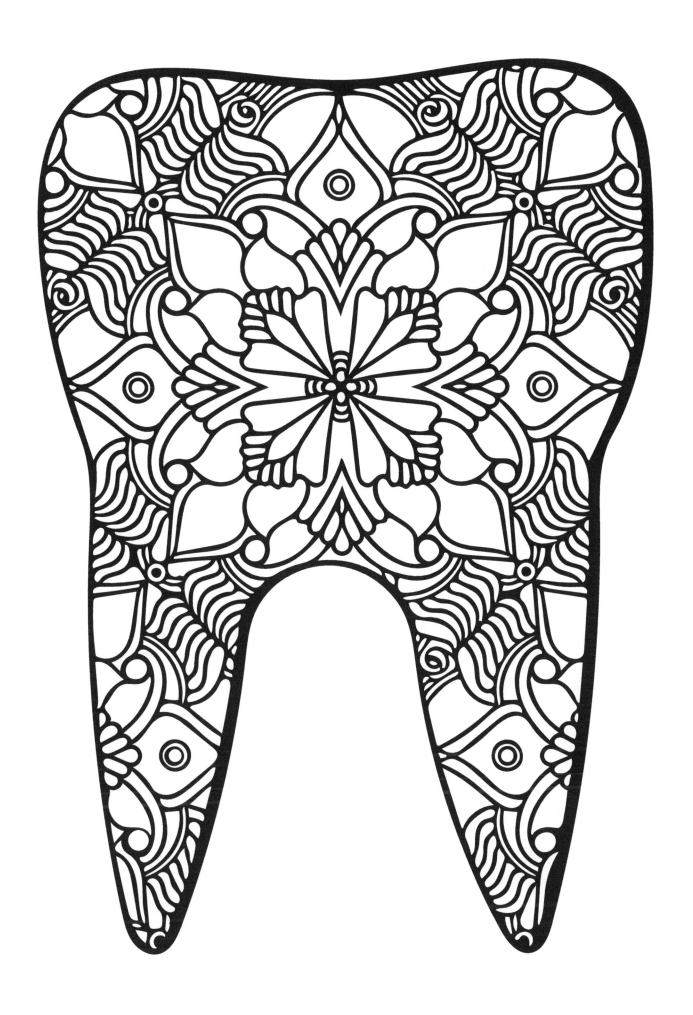

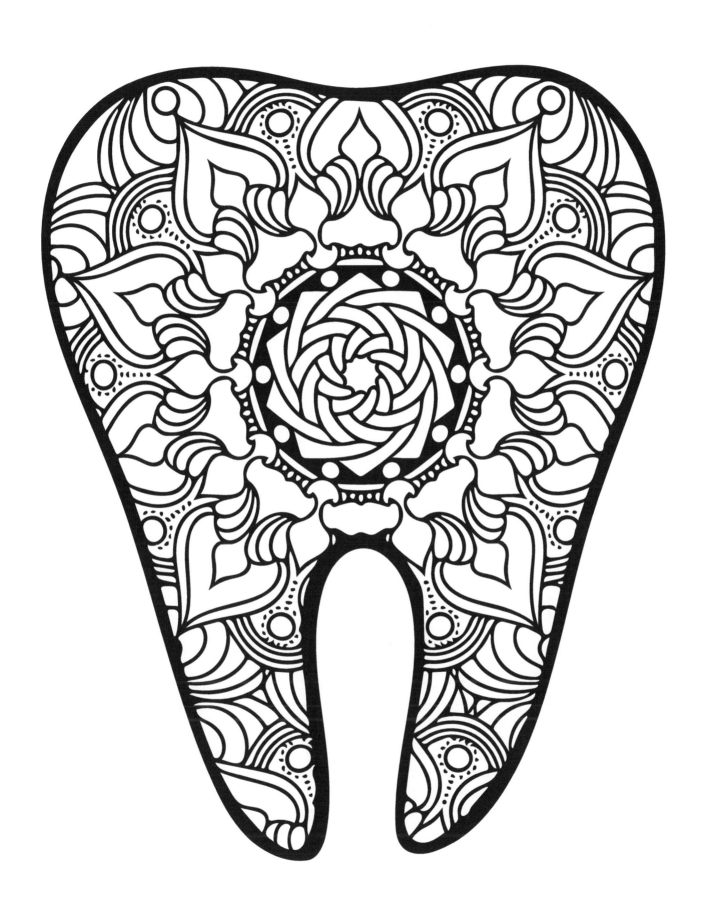

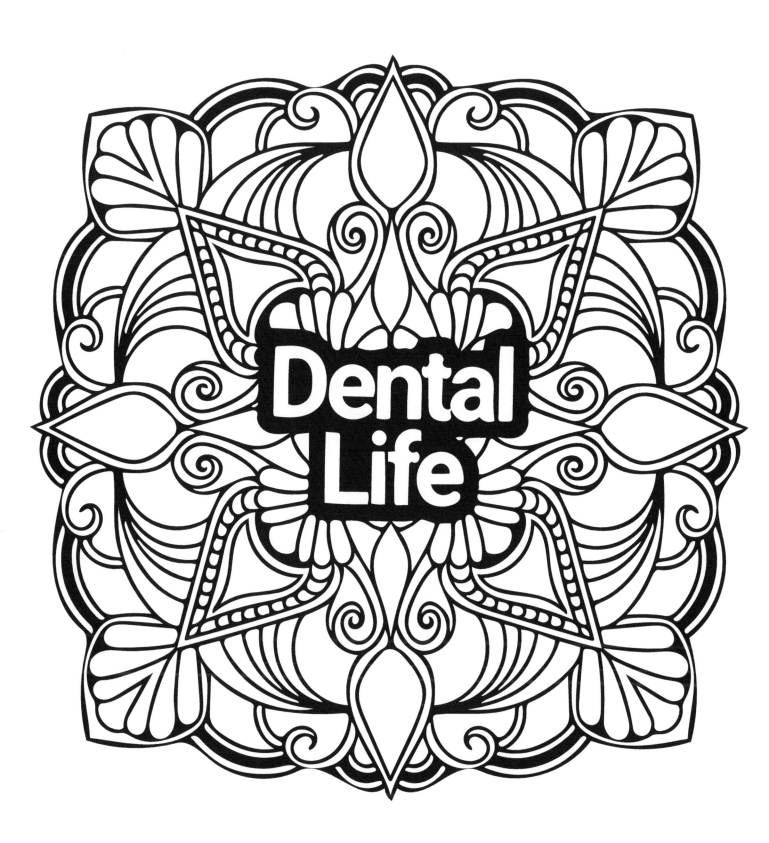

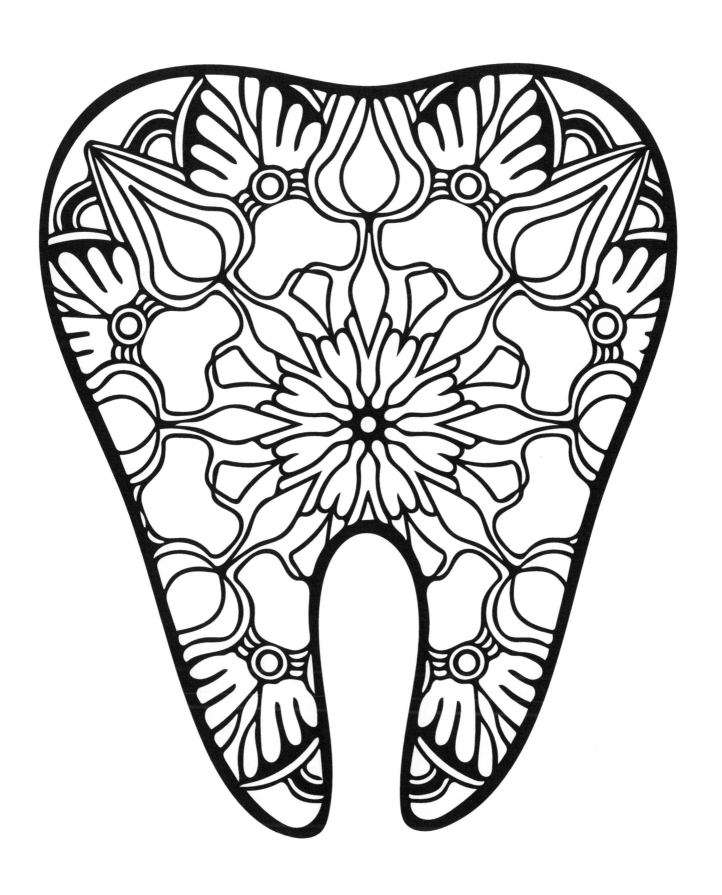

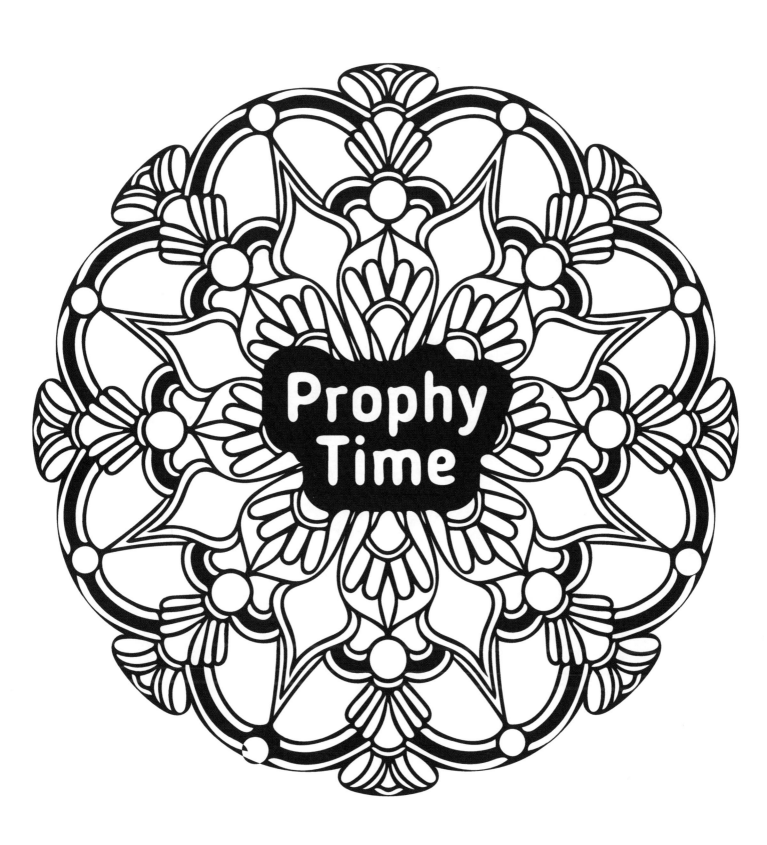

Made in United States
Troutdale, OR
02/24/2024